Treasure Island

Robert Louis Stevenson

Retold by
Ken Methold

LEVEL 3

Series Editor: Ken Methold

Treasure Island

Robert Louis Stevenson

Retold by Ken Methold

© 2009 Compass Publishing

Series Editor: Ken Methold
Acquisitions Editor: John Thomas
Copy Editor: Paul Edmunds
Illustrator: Bun Heang Ung
Cover/Interior Design: Design Plus

http://www.compasspub.com
email: info@compasspub.com

9 10 11 12 13 14 15 - BA - 2017 2016 2015 2014

ISBN: 978-1-59966-229-9

Printed in Korea

Contents

CHAPTER 1

An Unwanted Guest

Preview Questions

1. From the title, what do you think this chapter will be about?
2. Where do people find places to stay while they are traveling?
3. What type of work does a sailor do?

My story begins when an old **sailor** came to the **Admiral** Benbow. That is the name of the inn where I lived with my father. My father was the innkeeper.

"Do many people come here?" the old sailor asked my father.

"No," my father told him. "It is a very quiet place."

"Good," the old sailor said. "Then it is the place for me."

"And what is your name, sir?" my father asked him.

"Just call me 'captain,'" the man said.

He put some gold coins on the table. "Tell me when I have spent all these," he said. Then he went up to the room my father had for him.

Not long after he came to the inn, the Captain said to me, "Do you want to earn some money?"

"Yes, please," I answered. I was only a boy at the time and never had any money. "What do you want me to do?"

"Keep watch for a man with one leg," he said. "Tell me as soon as you see him. Do that and I'll give you a coin every week."

At first, the Captain was a very quiet man and did not

want to talk to anyone. But there were nights when he drank a lot of **rum**. Then he talked a lot and became very noisy. He also told stories to the men in the **bar** of the inn. They were stories about bad men doing bad things.

The more rum the Captain drank, the angrier he became. He shouted and used bad language. He sang the same song over and over again at the top of his voice,

"Fifteen men on the dead man's **chest**. Yo-ho-ho! And a bottle of rum."

My father wanted him to leave because some visitors stopped coming to the inn. They were afraid of him. My father was afraid of him, too. So, even when the gold was all spent, my father did not tell him to leave.

Then my father became ill, and Dr. Livesey came to see him. After giving my father some medicine, the doctor came into the bar. While the doctor waited for a man to bring his horse, the Captain started singing.

"Fifteen men on a dead man's chest. Yo-ho-ho! And a bottle of rum," he sang at the top of his voice.

The doctor was not pleased. He asked the Captain to be quiet. "There's a sick man here," he said.

The Captain took out his knife and pointed it at the doctor.

"Put that knife down, man," the doctor said. "And if you keep drinking rum, you'll soon be dead."

The Captain was very angry. He began to move toward the doctor. But the doctor was not afraid of him.

"Keep away from me," he said. "I am a **magistrate**, and if you do anything bad, you will be in trouble."

Then the doctor's horse came, and he rode away from

the inn. For a few days after this, the Captain was quiet.

Review Questions

1. What did the Captain ask the boy to do?
2. Why did a doctor come to the inn?
3. Why was the Captain singing and making noise?

CHAPTER
2

A Visit from Black Dog

Preview Questions

1. Who do you think might come to the inn?
2. Why do you think the Captain won't be pleased to see this man?
3. What do you think will make the Captain ill?

My father did not get better, and I had to do more work in the inn. One morning as I was getting breakfast, a man came in. He had two legs, but he had two fingers missing from his left hand. He asked for rum, and I sold him some.

"Is my friend Bill staying here?" he asked.

"I don't know anyone called Bill," I answered.

"What about 'Captain'?" he asked. "He has a cut on the right side of his face."

"Yes," I said. "A man we call 'Captain' is staying here. He has a cut on his face. But he is out now."

"Where is he?"

"I don't know," I said, "but he usually goes for a walk to the rock."

"The rock!" he said. "Ah, yes. That's where he'll be."

He laughed, but it was not a friendly laugh.

"I'll wait here for him," he said, and he hid behind the door.

I did not know what to do. "This man is not a friend of the Captain," I thought. I tried to leave the inn to tell the Captain about the man, but he stopped me.

"You do as I say," he said. "Sit here and keep your mouth shut. I want to give the Captain a surprise."

Soon the Captain came back to the inn. As he walked through the door, the stranger said, "Hello, Bill!"

The Captain was not pleased to see the man.

"Black Dog!" he cried. "What do you want?"

"I just wanted to talk to an old friend," the stranger said, then he turned to me. "Bring us rum," he ordered. "Then leave us alone."

I brought the men rum and then went away. I tried to hear what they were saying, but I could not. Then they began shouting at one another. I heard the Captain say, "No, no, it's finished. If one of us must hang, then all of us must."

Then the two men began fighting with their knives. The Captain cut Black Dog's shoulder. Then Black Dog ran away as fast as he could.

The Captain came back into the inn.

"Are you all right, Captain?" I asked him.

"Bring me rum, Jim," he said. "Then I must get out of here."

I went to get rum for him, but there was a sudden crash. I looked round. The Captain was lying on the floor.

At this moment, my mother came in. "Get the doctor," she said.

I ran to get Dr. Livesey.

After a while, the doctor came and looked at the Captain. I asked, "Is he **wounded**?"

"No," Dr. Livesey replied. "He has a bad heart."

He took off the Captain's coat. On his arm there was a picture of a man. He was hanging from a **gallows**. There were words, too. "Billy Bones," "Here's luck," and "A good wind."

The Captain opened his eyes. "Where's Black Dog?" he asked.

"He's gone, Billy Bones," the doctor told him.

"My name's not Billy Bones," the Captain said.

"Well, whatever your name is," the doctor said, "you'll die if you don't stop drinking rum."

And with these words the doctor went to see my father who was still very ill in bed.

Review Questions

1. What was the Captain's name?
2. What was the name of the man with only two fingers on one hand?
3. What caused the Captain to become ill?

Blind Pew Delivers a "Black Spot"

Preview Questions

1. Do you think Blind Pew is a good or bad person?
2. What do you think the black spot is?
3. What do you think the Captain is afraid of?

The Captain was ill and had to stay in bed. I took a drink to his room.

"Jim," he said to me. "You're a good boy. And I've been good to you. I've given you money, haven't I?"

"Yes, Captain," I said.

"Then bring me rum," he asked.

"It will kill you," I said. "I'll bring you one glass of rum. No more."

I brought him the rum. He drank

it quickly. Then he said, "I can't stay here. I must get up."

He tried to get out of bed, but he was not strong enough. He closed his eyes and lay back in bed for a few minutes. Then he said, "That Black Dog who was here. He's a bad one. Don't trust him. He and the others, they want my chest. They'll give me the black spot if I can't get away from them. You must help me, Jim. Only I know the secret place. Captain Flint told me about it as he was dying. Watch out for Black Dog and a man with one leg, Jim. I'll give you the treasure."

I didn't know what he was talking about. I wanted to ask him questions, but he fell asleep.

That night, my father died. I did not think about the Captain. I had other things to think about. Then a few days later, another strange man came to the inn. His clothes were very old. He was blind and carried a stick.

"Can anyone tell me where I am?" he asked.

"This is the Admiral Benbow Inn," I said, "at Black Hill Cove."

"Good. Now give me your hand, young man," he said, "and take me inside."

He took my hand and held it very tightly. "Now take me to the Captain," he said in a cruel voice.

"No, sir," I answered. "I will not."

He held my hand even tighter. "Take me to the Captain, or I'll break your arm," he said.

I did not want to obey him, but he was hurting me. I led him to the Captain's room. When the Captain saw him, he looked very afraid and whispered, "Blind Pew."

"Hello, Bill," the blind man said. "I've got something

for you."

Then he said to me, "Take his left hand and bring it to my right."

I obeyed him. He passed something from his hand into the Captain's hand. Then he turned and quickly left the room. He went down the stairs and left the inn.

The Captain looked at his hand and then cried out. "He's given me the black spot. We've only got six hours," he cried.

He tried to stand, but he fell to the floor. I ran to him. He did not move or speak. He was dead.

My mother came into the room and saw the Captain on the floor.

"What happened, Jim?" she said.

"A blind man came into the room and gave him something," I said. "The Captain was afraid. He knew he was in danger."

"In what way?" my mother asked.

"Some men—Black Dog was one—wanted something in his chest," I said. "He knew a secret place. I don't know what it was or where. He was afraid of getting the black spot."

"What black spot?" my mother asked.

"I don't know, mother," I said, "but we should leave here. The Captain said something about having only six hours."

"We'll go to the next village," my mother said. "Then perhaps someone will get Dr. Livesey, and he can explain."

Review Questions
1. What happened to Jim's father?
2. What did the blind man give to the Captain?
3. Why was the Captain afraid of the black spot?

CHAPTER 4

Inside a Dead Man's Chest

Preview Questions

1. Why do you think Jim and his mother leave the inn?
2. What do you think Jim will find in the Captain's chest?
3. Why do you think the blind man and other men will come back to the inn?

The next village was very near, and we were soon talking to some people there. Many of them knew about Captain Flint. They were afraid.

My mother said, "The dead man owes us money. I'm going back to open his chest and take what he owes me. Who'll come with us?"

No one moved or spoke.

"I'll give the boy a pistol," one man said.

"I'll ride to Dr. Livesey's," another man said.

This was all the help we could get from them. We went back to the inn and locked the door and windows.

The Captain was lying on his stomach in his bedroom. There was a small piece of paper on the floor near his hand. It was black on one side. On the other side were the words, "*You have until ten o'clock tonight.*"

I used a knife to open the chest. Inside the chest there were some clothes, two pistols, and coins from many different countries. At the bottom of the box there was a piece of cloth wrapped around some papers.

My mother counted out the coins the Captain owed her.

I picked up the papers wrapped in cloth. Then we heard a noise. It was the sound of the blind man's stick—tap, tap—tapping on the road outside the inn. It came nearer and nearer. Then it stopped. It started again, but this time it was moving away.

"He may not be able to see us," I said, "but soon other men will come and find us. Black Dog perhaps. Or the man with one leg."

"It's only seven o'clock," my mother said. "I haven't finished counting my money."

"There's no time, Mother," I said. "We must go before the men come."

As we left the inn, I heard the sound of running feet. "They're coming, Mother," I said. "Run quickly."

"I can't, Jim," my mother said. "I feel ill."

There was a bridge just outside the inn. I pulled my mother under the bridge. We waited there as the men came nearer. There were seven or eight of them. Blind Pew was one of the men. The night was dark by now, but one of the men had a light.

"Break down the door," he said.

Three of the men broke down the door. They ran inside. Then one of them shouted, "Bill's dead!"

Another man shouted, "The chest's open. Someone's opened it. But there are coins inside."

"We don't want the coins," the blind man shouted. "Where's Captain Flint's map?"

"It's not here," a man said.

"And there's nothing on Bill," another man shouted.

"It's that boy!" the blind man shouted. "We must find him. Look everywhere in the house."

There was a lot of noise as the men looked everywhere in the house for me. The men began to quarrel. Blind Pew hit one of them with his stick. Then there was the sound of horses coming toward the inn. The men ran off, leaving Pew behind.

"Don't leave me," he shouted. "Black Dog, don't leave old Pew."

The horses had arrived at the inn. Pew tried to run from them, but he could not see where he was going. He fell under one of the horses and died.

Review Questions

1. Where did Jim and his mother hide?
2. Why were the men angry?
3. Why did the men want to find Jim?

Squire Trelawney Has a Plan

Preview Questions

1. What kind of men do you think Pew and his friends are?
2. What kind of man do you think the old captain was?
3. What do you think the squire will find wrapped in the cloth?

The horsemen were government men. Pew and his friends were **smugglers**. They had a boat not far away. They got to the boat in time and took it out to sea.

The head government man, Mr. Dance, came back with us to the Admiral Benbow. I told him about the Captain and the sea chest.

"What were they looking for?" Mr. Dance asked.

"I don't know," I said. "Perhaps it was this." I showed him the cloth with the papers in it.

"I'll take it," he said.

"I want Dr. Livesey to have it," I said. "He is a magistrate."

"You are right," Mr. Dance answered. He spoke to one of his men. "Let this boy ride behind you," he said.

I got onto the horse, and we all rode away from the inn.

We found out that Dr. Livesey was visiting **Squire** Trelawney, so it was to his house that we rode. The squire was in his library with the doctor.

"What's this about?" the doctor asked.

Mr. Dance told him his story. The doctor and the squire listened in silence. When Mr. Dance finished, the squire said, "You have done well, Mr. Dance. And you, Jim Hawkins, are a **brave** boy. Do you have the papers in the piece of cloth?"

"Yes, sir," I said, and I gave them to him.

"Good," the doctor said. Then he turned to the squire.

"Squire," he said, "the government men must go. They have government business to do. I'd like Jim to stay here."

Mr. Dance and the other government men left.

"Do you know anything about this Captain Flint?" the doctor asked the squire.

"Oh, yes," the squire said. "I was on a ship that he attacked. He is a dangerous **pirate**. He killed many men and stole their treasure."

"Perhaps then," the doctor said, "he buried the stolen treasure. And perhaps these papers will tell us where it is."

"If they do," the squire said, "then the three of us will go to Bristol. I can get a ship there to take us to look for it."

The doctor took a book and map out from the piece of cloth. The squire studied the book.

"This book has the names all the ships Captain Flint attacked and how much money he stole from them. He died a rich man. Now let me see the map."

The doctor handed it to the squire. The map was of an island about twelve kilometers long and eight kilometers wide. There was a hill in the middle. On the hill were the words "*The Spy-Glass.*" There were three crosses in red ink: two in the north of the island and one in the south-west. Next to the last cross were the words, "*Most of the treasure here.*" On the back of the paper were the words, "*Tall tree. Look through Spy-Glass to a point north of north, north east. Skeleton Island east, south east by east.*"

There were more words that I did not understand, but the squire knew what they meant. He said to the doctor, "This is all the information we need. We will go to this island. You will come as the ship's doctor, and Jim shall be the **cabin boy**."

"Very well, Trelawney," the doctor said, "but there is one man I am afraid of."

"Oh? And who is that, sir?" the squire wanted to know.

"You, sir," the doctor said. "You don't know how to keep a secret. There will be men who will do anything to get this map. You must tell no one that we have it."

"I **promise**," the squire said. "You have my word."

Review Questions

1. Why did the squire suggest they go to Bristol?
2. What will Jim's work be on the ship?
3. What did the doctor make the squire promise?

Long John Silver Takes Charge

The next day, Squire Trelawney went to Bristol. I stayed at the squire's house, waiting for news of the ship. Every day I studied the map, learning everything on it. I wanted to remember everything about it.

At last, a letter came from the squire. He wrote: *"I have a good ship, and she is ready to sail. Her name is the* Hispaniola. *Everyone here has helped me. They are as excited as I am about the reason for our journey."*

"I don't like this. He has told people about the treasure," I thought. I remembered Dr. Livesey saying, "There is only one man I am afraid of." This was the squire because he could not keep a secret.

I read on: *"I bought the ship from an old friend, Blandly. Many people here do not like him. They say he will do anything for money. They say I paid too much for the ship. But I believe Blandly is honest. I didn't like the crew, though, so I looked for other men. They were difficult to find. Then I met an old sailor, Long John Silver. I believe he has a wife here and is not poor. "I'll get you a* **crew**," *Long John Silver said. "I'll get you the best crew there is. But I want to sail with you." He has only one leg, so I said, "You can be the* *ship's cook." He was happy about this. Within a few days, he found me a crew. He didn't like those I already had either, so I let them go. And now we are ready to sail."*

That next morning, I went home to the Admiral Benbow to say goodbye to my mother. Tom Redruth, one of the squire's men, came with me.

The next evening, we took the **coach** to Bristol. It was a busy city. There were many ships, and there were sailors everywhere.

Squire Trelawney was staying at an inn. It was near where the ship was waiting to sail. Tom and I found the squire on the ship.

"Welcome, Jim," he said. "The doctor came last night, so now we are ready. We can sail tomorrow."

"Take this letter to Long John Silver," he said. "He's staying at The Spy-glass Inn. He owns it."

I found the inn easily. It was full of sailors. As I walked toward it, a man came out. He had only one leg.

"Are you Long John Silver?" I asked him.

"I am, young man. And who are you?" he said.

"Jim Hawkins," I said. "The cabin boy on the *Hispaniola*."

I gave him the squire's letter. As I did so, another man came out of the inn. I knew who he was. He had two fingers missing on his left hand.

"That's Black Dog!" I cried.

Black Dog ran off.

"Catch him, Ben!" Long John Silver shouted to one of the men in the inn. "He owes me money."

Then he turned to me. "Who did you say he was?"

"Black Dog," I said. "Didn't Squire Trelawney tell you

about him and the other men?"

"He did! But I didn't know the man. I've never seen him before." He turned to one of the men who was coming out of the inn.

"Have you seen that man before, Morgan?" he asked him.

"No, sir," Morgan answered.

"Do you know his name?"

"No, sir," Morgan replied.

Long John Silver was thoughtful. "Perhaps I have seen the man before. He came here once with a blind man."

"Blind Pew," I said. "He was one of the men who came to the Admiral Benbow."

"Aye," Long John Silver said. "I remember him now. I didn't trust him."

At first I didn't trust Long John Silver. "What was Black Dog doing at the Spy-glass Inn?" I asked myself. "Was Long John Silver telling me the truth?"

Then Ben came back.

"I couldn't catch him," he said. "He was too fast for me."

Long John was now angry. "Let's go and tell Squire Trelawney what's happened," he said. "He'll want to know."

We went to the inn where the squire and doctor were staying. Long John told them about Black Dog and Blind Pew.

"And I sent Ben to catch Black Dog, didn't I, Jim?" Long John said.

"Yes," I said, "you did. But he got away."

"There's nothing we can do about it," the squire said. "We'll sail this afternoon. Tell the crew to be on the ship by four o'clock."

"I'll do that," Long John Silver answered and walked away.

"We're lucky to have that man on our crew," the squire said. "He's going to be very useful." He smiled. "Now let's go to the ship and make sure everything is ready."

Review Questions

1. Why did Jim think the squire had told people in Bristol about the treasure?
2. How did Jim know that Black Dog was the man at the Spy-glass Inn?
3. What do you think Black Dog was doing at the Spy-glass Inn?

CHAPTER 7

Captain Smollett Is Worried

Preview Questions

1. Who do you think Captain Smollett is?
2. Why do you think Captain Smollett is worried?
3. Where do you think the *Hispaniola* will sail to?

The *Hispaniola* was far out to sea, so we went to her by small boat. We were welcomed on board by the mate, Arrow. He was very friendly with Squire Trelawney.

The captain, a man called Smollett, was not so friendly. He asked to speak to the squire in his **cabin.**

"Is everything ready, Captain?" the squire asked him.

"I will speak honestly to you, sir," Captain Smollett said. "I don't like where we are going, and I don't like the crew. And I do not like Arrow, the mate."

The squire was angry. "Perhaps you don't like the ship." he said.

"I don't know if I do or don't. I haven't sailed on her before," the captain said.

"Then perhaps you don't like me," the squire said, very angry now.

Dr. Livesey said, "Please, let's not argue. But, Captain, tell me more."

"Very well, sir," Captain Smollett said. "Everyone on this ship knows more about where we are going than I do. You have told me nothing. I know only what I hear from the crew. That's not good, sir. I am the captain of this ship.

I should know more than the crew."

"You are right," Dr. Livesey said.

"They say we are going to look for treasure," Captain Smollett **continued**. "I don't like that. There is always trouble with treasure. And I don't like secrets. Huh! Some secret! Even Silver's **parrot** knows."

I remembered seeing Long John Silver with a parrot on his shoulder.

"To be honest with you both," Captain Smollett said, "I don't think you know what you are doing. There's a lot of trouble ahead for you."

"We are not as **ignorant** as you think, Captain," Dr. Livesey said. "But tell me, why you don't like the crew?"

"I know nothing about them, but I should have been able to choose my own crew. That's for a captain to do."

"And what about Arrow?" the doctor said.

"He's not a good mate," Captain Smollett said. "He's too friendly with the crew. I can't trust him."

"Tell us what you want, Captain?" the doctor said.

"I want the guns and **gunpowder** kept under my cabin. I want you and your friends to stay at this end of the ship."

"Very well," the squire said. "Anything more?"

"Yes. There's been too much talk about the treasure."

"I agree," the doctor said. "Far too much."

"The crew knows about the map. They know where the island is," Captain Smollett said.

"I never told anyone about that," the squire said, but neither the doctor nor I believed him.

"You are worried about a **mutiny**, aren't you, Captain?" the doctor asked.

"Yes, Doctor. I am the captain of this ship, and I must keep it safe," Captain Smollett said. "If you won't agree to what I have asked for, you will have to get another captain."

The squire looked at him for a long time. Then he said, "Very well. I agree. Do what you must."

Captain Smollett left the cabin.

"I don't like that man," the squire said. "He is a trouble-maker."

The doctor did not agree. "I think there are only two honest men on board with us," he said, "the captain and Long John Silver."

Review Questions

1. What was Captain Smollett worried about?
2. Why didn't Captain Smollett think Arrow was a good mate?
3. Do you think the doctor is wrong about Long John Silver?

Long John Silver Plans a Mutiny

Preview Questions

1. What do you think Jim will find out about Long John Silver?
2. What do you think will happen to Arrow?
3. In what ways do you think the squire is sometimes foolish?

The next morning, we began our journey. Long John Silver began to sing as we moved out to sea. "Fifteen men on the dead man's chest," he sang. "Yo-ho-ho and a bottle of rum."

And then all the crew sang as well, "Yo-ho-ho and a bottle of rum."

I knew the song. The old captain used to sing it at the Admiral Benbow.

The ship was strong and the weather fine, so we had a good journey. Only Arrow, the mate, caused trouble. He was **drunk** most of the time. Then one night, he fell into the sea and disappeared. Captain Smollett was not unhappy about this. He made John Anderson, a good sailor, the ship's mate in Arrow's place.

Another good sailor was Israel Hands. He was a friend of Long John Silver. All the crew liked Long John Silver because he had many stories to tell. He was always very kind to me.

"Come and sit with me, Jim," he often said. "And say hello to Captain Flint."

This was the name of his parrot. It was a noisy bird that

was always talking. It didn't know many words, so it said the same ones again and again.

The squire and Captain Smollett kept away from one another. They did not like one another.

"Smollett was wrong about the crew," the squire said. "He'll be wrong about other things."

Then the squire made the captain angry by giving the men rum and apples from the **barrel**.

Captain Smollett spoke to Dr. Livesey about it. "It's not good to give the men these things," he said. "The time will come when he will be sorry he did."

But the apple barrel soon became very important.

One night when we were very near the island I went to the

barrel to get an apple. I was tired and after eating an apple, I sat down in the barrel. There I fell asleep. It was not long before a voice awoke me. A man was sitting near the barrel. It was Long John Silver. He was talking to a young sailor called Dick. He was telling him about his days sailing with the dead Captain Flint. He told him about the life of a pirate.

As he spoke, I realized that Long John Silver was as bad as Black Dog and Blind Pew and other pirates who sailed with him.

Then Israel Hands came up.

"When are we going to take over the ship?" he wanted to know.

"As soon as we get to the island," Silver said. "Then we'll make the squire and doctor take us to the treasure."

"What will you do with them afterward?" Dick asked.

"Kill them," Silver answered. Then he said to the boy, "Dick, get me an apple out of the barrel."

I did not know what to do. I knew that if the boy saw me, Silver or Israel Hands would kill me.

Then Hands stopped the boy. "You don't want an apple, John," he said. "You need rum. We all need rum."

He sent Dick off to get the rum. He soon came back, and the three of them began to drink. And then, the voice of the lookout cried, "Land ho!"

Review Questions

1. Why did Jim go to the apple barrel?
2. What did Jim hear at the apple barrel?
3. Why didn't Long John Silver discover Jim at the apple barrel?

CHAPTER 9

Jim Tells All

Preview Questions

1. Who do you think will decide where the ship should anchor?
2. What do you think Jim must do?
3. Why do you think Captain Smollett won't return to Bristol?

Everyone ran to one side of the ship and looked toward the land.

"Has anyone ever been to this island?" Captain Smollett asked.

"I have, sir," Long John Silver answered. "I was the cook on a ship that came here."

"Where is a good place for us to anchor?" the captain asked.

"On the south of the island. Skeleton Island, people call it. There were once pirates here," Silver said.

"Thank you, Silver," Captain Smollett said. "You may go. I may need you to help me later."

I was surprised Silver showed that he knew about the island. I walked up to the doctor.

"Doctor," I said. "I must talk to you and Squire Trelawney and the captain. I have very bad news. You must listen to me. I must speak to you all in secret."

"Very well, Jim," he said. Then the doctor walked over to the squire and the captain and spoke to them. The captain spoke to the crew.

"You have all worked well," he said. "We have found

the island. Now, Squire Trelawney wants you all to have a drink. I am going to have one with him and the doctor. We are going to drink to your health in my cabin."

The doctor, the squire, and the captain went to the captain's cabin. A few minutes later, the captain shouted, "Cabin boy!"

I ran to his cabin. None of the crew asked me why. They knew I was the cabin boy.

When I went into the cabin, the squire said, "What's this all about, Hawkins?"

I told them what I heard Silver say to Dick and Israel Hands.

"There will be a mutiny then," the captain said.

"Yes, sir. That's Silver's plan."

The squire said, "I am to **blame**. You were right about the crew, Captain."

"Yes, but wrong about Silver. I'll make that man hang," Captain Smollett said.

"What must we do?" the doctor asked.

"We must go on. We mustn't turn back," the captain said. "If we turn back, the crew will know why and mutiny now. We have a little time. They won't mutiny until we have led them to the treasure. There are only four of us. How many of the men can we trust?"

"Only the three men I brought from my home," Squire Trelawney said.

"Then there are only seven of us," the captain said. "We need to find out what the **mutineers'** plans are."

"Jim can help us do that," the doctor said. "He can move about the ship without anyone asking why."

"Our safety is in your hands then, Jim," the squire said.

"I will do my best, sir," I said.

But I was afraid. We were only seven, and one of us was me—a boy. There were nineteen men who would probably join a mutiny.

Review Questions

1. What were nineteen of the men planning to do?
2. How many men could the squire now trust?
3. Why was the safety of the squire and his men in Jim's hands?

CHAPTER

10

Jim Meets Ben Gunn

Preview Questions

1. Why do you think Captain Smollett must be careful with what he says to the crew?
2. Why do you think Captain Smollett wanted the guns and powder kept in his cabin?
3. Who do you think Ben Gunn is?

Now that we were near land, the crew did not want to do any work.

The captain said, "I must be careful what I say to the men. If I am too hard on them they will mutiny now. Silver was a fool to tell them about the treasure. They are only going to think about finding it."

"Silver is in danger, too, isn't he?" the doctor asked. "He got them here. But now they don't need him any more."

"That's true," the squire answered. "But he seems to know how to make the men obey him. He doesn't want any trouble yet. Perhaps we should let him take charge of them."

"We'll let the men go ashore," the captain said. "Silver can be in charge of them. If all the men go, then we can take the ship away from the island. If only half of them go, we can stop any mutiny."

He turned to me. "Hawkins," he said, "ask Hunter, Joyce, and Redruth to come here."

"Yes, sir," I said. These were the squire's men. They were

the only three men we could trust.

When they came into the captain's cabin, he said, "I believe there may be a mutiny."

"I thought something was wrong, Captain," Redruth said. "The men are talking among themselves about treasure."

"We must each carry a gun," the captain said. He handed each of them a gun and powder. Then he went out of the cabin to talk to the crew.

"Men," he said, "it's a hot day and you are tired. I know you want to get away from the ship for a while and go to the island."

"Aye, we do!" the men shouted.

"Then Silver will take as many boats as you need. I'll fire a gun when it is time for you to come back."

The men ran to the boats. They were thinking they would find the treasure as soon as they got to the land.

Thirteen men left the ship in two boats. Silver was in one of the boats. Six men stayed on the *Hispaniola.*

"The captain, doctor, squire, and his three men can look after the six crew men," I thought. "They won't need me. I have a plan."

I jumped into one of the boats as it pulled away from the ship.

As soon as the boat neared the shore, I jumped out and ran off as fast as I could.

I ran about the island for quite some time. I wanted to get as far away from Silver and his men as I could. But then, when I was sure they were not running after me, I hid for a while behind a tree.

It was not long before I heard voices. One of them was

Silver's. I moved slowly toward the sound of the voice. I stayed behind the trees. When the men were near, I listened to what they said.

"You must be careful, Tom," Silver was saying. "The others will kill you if you don't join them."

"You're a good man, Silver," the other man was saying. "You're honest and brave. And you don't need money. You don't need to be part of the mutiny. And I won't be. No, John. I'll have nothing to do with it."

Just then, I heard a shout. It was followed by a loud scream.

Tom jumped up. "What was that?" he shouted.

"Oh, that must be Alan," Silver said, with a cruel smile.

"Alan! He's a good man. And your crew have killed him, haven't they?" the man called Tom said. And with this he turned away from Silver and began to walk away.

He did not get far. Silver took out his knife and threw it. It hit Tom in the back, and he fell to the ground.

"Two of the good men on the crew were dead. How many more will die?" I thought. "When the captain fires the gun, the crew will go back to the ship. There will be more killing."

Afraid for my life and for the lives of my friends, I ran deep into the forest.

As I ran, I saw something move in the trees in front of me. I did not know who or what it was. I knew only that behind me were Silver and the other killers. In front, there was probably danger. Then a man came out of the trees. He was thin and dirty.

"Who are you?" I shouted.

"Ben Gunn," he answered. "You are the first person I have seen for three years."

"How did you get here?" I asked him. "Did something happen to your ship?"

"My ship sailed away without me. Since then I have lived on what I could find in the forest and in the sea."

He asked my name. "Jim," I told him. "Jim Hawkins."

"Well, Jim," he said. "I'm sure you are a good young man. If you help me, I'll help you. I'm rich, and I can make you rich, too."

Then he asked, "You're not from Captain Flint's ship, are you?"

"No," I said. "Captain Flint is dead. But some of his men are on my ship."

"Does one of them have only one leg?" Ben Gunn asked.

"Yes," I said. "Long John Silver. He's only the cook, but the men follow him."

"Do you?" Ben Gunn asked.

I told him my story. I told him about Squire Trelawney and Dr. Livesey. "They are good men," I said. "I trust them, and so can you."

"Then I'll tell you my story," he said. "I was one of Captain Flint's men. Our ship was *The Walrus*. When we came to this island, he brought his treasure here and buried it. He took six men to help him. When he came back, he was alone."

"He killed the six men!" I said.

"Yes. I don't know how he did it, but he did. Silver and Billy Bones were on *The Walrus*. They asked Flint about his treasure. 'It's buried on the island,' he said. 'You can go and look for it if you like, but *The Walrus* sails now.' Well, no one wanted to stay on the island, so we all stayed on the ship and sailed away. Three years later, I was on another ship. As we came to the island, I told the captain and crew about Flint's treasure."

"Did they find it?" I asked.

"No," Ben Gunn said. "They looked for it for twelve days. They were really angry with me. 'We're going,' they said, 'but you can stay and keep looking.' And they sailed away leaving me here. If you help me, you and your friends can share the treasure with me."

"But how can I get back to the *Hispaniola*?" I asked.

"I have a small boat. I made it with my own hands," Ben Gunn said. "It will take us to the boat."

Just then I heard a gun fire. And then, not far away in the forest, I saw my ship's flag.

Review Questions

1. Who did Jim find in the forest?
2. What did this person tell Jim?
3. Why do you think Ben Gunn is important in this story?

Safe in the Stockade

Preview Questions

1. Why do you think Jim can't tell this part of the story?
2. Do you think Ben Gunn is a good person?
3. What is a stockade?

Dr. Livesey writes:

It was about one thirty when Silver and his men left the *Hispaniola*. On the ship were Captain Smollett, the squire and the squire's three men, and myself. There were also six of the crew. We thought about locking up the crew and sailing the ship away ourselves. We had guns, and they did not, so it would have been easy to lock them up. But there was no wind. Then Hunter, one of our men, told us that Jim Hawkins was not on the ship.

"We must find out what has happened to Jim," I said to the squire. "I'll go with Hunter to the island and find out what I can."

We took one of the small boats to the island. On the island, two of Silver's men were **guarding** their boats. I thought they were going to stop us, but they did not.

We walked into the forest. To my surprise, we soon came to a **stockade** made from trees.

"I don't know who built this," I said to Hunter. "but it will be difficult to attack. They have guns. And they'll have not only food they took from the ship but also water. Look!"

I pointed to a small river. It went into the stockade. "And that's more than we have on the ship," I said. "We have food, but we do not have any drinking water left."

I was thinking about this when I heard a cry. "Jim Hawkins has been killed," I thought.

"We must get back to the ship," I told Hunter. We ran back to our boat and were soon on the *Hispaniola* again.

I had a plan. I told it to Trelawney and Captain Smollett.

"There is a stockade on the island," I said. "The mutineers are all out looking for the treasure. We can move into the stockade. We can take food from the ship and guns and powder. We'll be safer there than on the ship."

The squire and the captain agreed.

The captain took out his pistol and shouted at the crew.

"If any one of you makes a wrong move," he said, "I'll shoot you dead."

We made five journeys from the ship to the island and back. We took food, pistols, and powder on each journey. Just before we left the *Hispaniola* for our fifth journey, Captain Smollett shouted to one of the crew, "Abraham Gray! Listen to me."

Gray was one of the six crew left on the ship.

"I know you're a good man, Gray," the captain shouted. "Come with us."

No one moved inside the cabin.

"I'll count to ten, Gray," the captain shouted. "If you're not with us by ten, you'll die with the other mutineers."

There were shouts from inside the cabin and the noise of fighting. Then Gray ran out of the cabin. He had a bad cut on his face. As he jumped into the boat, he said, "I'm with you, Captain."

The next moment, we were moving away from the ship toward the island.

Then the captain remembered something.

"The **cannon**—the big gun—is on the *Hispaniola*!" he said. "If they can get that to the island, they can shoot a hole in the stockade. We won't be safe in there."

"They won't be able to get the cannon off the ship into a small boat," I said.

"Oh, yes they will," the captain said. "Look."

I turned and looked back at the ship. Five of the crew were getting ready to put the cannon into a boat. I remembered then that there was powder and shot for the gun still on the ship.

Abraham Gray said, "Israel Hands is one of the crew. He was Captain Flint's gunner. He knows how to shoot the cannon."

Captain Smollett asked, "Which of you two is the best shot?"

"Mr. Trelawney is a much better shot than I am, Captain," I said.

"Then, Mr. Trelawney, take my pistol and try to shoot Israel Hands."

We stopped rowing. The squire lifted the pistol. Then he fired. But just as he did so, Hands bent down. The shot went over his head.

"We must get ashore quickly," the captain said. "They'll shoot at us with the cannon."

We **rowed** as hard as we could. We rowed too hard. The boat over-turned, and we were all in the water. Luckily, it was not deep.

And now we heard shouts from the shore. Hearing the shot, Silver and his men ran toward the stockade.

"We must get to the stockade before them," I shouted. "Leave the boat."

We ran out of the sea toward the shore and the stockade. We left half of our food, pistols, and powder on the boat.

We had to cross open ground to get from the forest to the stockade. As we did so, seven of the mutineers ran toward us. Four of us had time to fire. One of the mutineers fell to the ground. The others ran back into the forest.

We ran toward the stockade. Just as we got to it, there was a shot. Tom Redruth fell to the ground.

"Tom! Tom!" the squire cried, "Are you all right?"

"I'm dying, sir," Tom said.

"I'm so sorry," the squire said. "This is all my fault."

Tom died.

We went into the stockade. Captain Smollett had two British flags. He flew one from the top of the house in the stockade. The other he put over Tom's body. Then he turned to me.

"What will happen if we do not get home?" he asked. "Will another ship come looking for us?"

"Yes," I said. "Mr. Blandly will send a ship to look for us."

"When will he do that?"

"In August."

"That is months away. We have enough food for ten days," the captain said.

Just then, the mutineers fired the cannon. A cannon ball fell into the stockade.

"Captain," the squire said. "They are shooting at your flag. Perhaps you should take it down."

"Never," said the captain. "They must not think that we are afraid of them."

I agreed with the captain.

Some of our stores were still outside the stockade. Gray and Hunter went outside to get them. But they were too late. The mutineers were carrying them away. Then I heard a voice calling. "Doctor! Squire! Captain!"

I turned. Jim Hawkins was climbing into the stockade.

Review Questions

1. What did the squire and his men take with them from the *Hispaniola*?
2. Where did they stay on the island?
3. What did the mutineers have that the squire and his men did not have?

⑫

Jim Returns

Preview Questions

1. Why do you think Silver comes to the stockade?
2. What do you think Silver and his men will do?
3. Who do you think Ben Gunn will help?

Jim continues:

When Ben Gunn saw the ship's flag, he said, "Your friends must be in the stockade. It's the British flag. Pirates fly the Jolly Roger—the skull and cross bones."

"Who built this stockade?" I asked him.

"Captain Flint," Ben said. "He was a clever man. He knew what he was doing."

"I must get to the stockade," I said.

Just then, one of the mutineers fired the cannon. The ball went over my head and into the stockade.

"It's not safe here," Ben Gunn said.

"I agree," I said. "We shall be safer with my friends. You wait here."

I ran through the forest to the back of the stockade. Then I climbed into it, calling, "Doctor! Squire! Captain! It's me, Jim!"

"Jim!" the doctor cried. He took my hand. "I am so happy to see you."

The squire and the captain also took my hand.

There was no time to talk. There was work to do. Two men went out to get wood for a fire. Two men buried poor

Tom Redruth. The doctor became our cook. I became the watchman. The captain made sure we all did our work.

The doctor came to talk to me.

"Captain Smollett is a fine man," he said. "We are lucky to have him. But tell me about this man, Ben Gunn."

"I think he may be mad, sir," I said. "He has been alone on this island for a long time."

"But will he help the mutineers?" the doctor wanted to know.

"No, sir," I said. "I think he will want to help us."

"Our best plan," the doctor said, "is to try and kill as many of the mutineers as we can. They have the cannon, but we have pistols and a lot of powder. They know that."

"What will they do?"

"I think they will probably take the ship."

There was a shout from outside the stockade. I looked over the wall.

"It's Silver," I said. "He's holding a white flag. He wants to talk. He's got only one man with him."

"Stay inside," the captain said to us. "This could be a trick." Then he shouted at Silver, "What do you want?"

"To talk to you," Silver said. "I'm coming in. I trust you not to shoot me."

And with these words, he began to climb into the stockade.

"Good morning, Doctor," he said. "Good morning, Jim. A good place you have here."

"Say what you must and then go," Captain Smollett said. "You're a mutineer and as bad as the rest."

"We don't want to make trouble for you," Silver said. "You have the map. We can find the treasure if we have that map. Give it to us, and we'll share the treasure with you. Then you can sail home with us. Or you can stay here, and I'll send a ship for you."

"Is that all you have to say?" Captain Smollett said.

"Yes. If you won't agree, then you're all dead men. We have the cannon. What's your answer?"

"We have the map," the Captain said, "and without it you can't find the treasure. You may have more men than we have, but none of them can sail a ship. Without us you can't leave this island. So go and tell that to your crew."

Silver was now very angry.

"I'll tell them," he shouted. "And before night, you'll all be dead men."

The man with the flag helped him to climb out of the stockade, and he moved quickly toward the trees.

Captain Smollett said, "Silver knows we shall never give him the map. If he is to get it, then he must take it from us. There will be an attack."

"Where will the attack come from?" the doctor asked. "There is forest all around us."

"We won't know until it comes," the captain said. "We must keep a lookout to the north, south, east, and west."

He sent us to our places. The doctor stood by the door. Hunter looked to the east. Joyce looked to the west. Gray kept watch on the north side. Each man had a pistol. The captain and I did not have pistols, though. Our work was to load the pistols with powder.

Time passed, then Joyce fired.

"They're coming!" he shouted.

The attack was on. The mutineers began firing from north, south, east, and west. Most of the firing was coming from the north.

"That's where the attack will come from," the captain said.

He was right. Four mutineers ran out of the forest toward the stockade. They climbed the wall. More mutineers ran out of the trees. Squire and Gray fired again and again. Three of these mutineers fell. The fourth ran back to the trees. But there were now four mutineers inside the stockade. There was no time to re-load the pistols.

Now it was hand to hand fighting. At last the mutineers ran off, leaving their dead. There were four outside the stockade and one inside. Of our men, Joyce was dead, Hunter was wounded and so was the captain.

"Have they all gone?" he asked.

"Yes," the doctor said. "But five are dead."

"Good," the captain said. "We are now stronger than we were before. We were seven to nineteen. There are now four of us to nine of them."

I learned later that we were four to eight. One of the wounded mutineers died.

Review Questions

1. What did Silver offer to do?
2. What could the captain and his men do that the mutineers could not do?
3. In what way has the situation changed?

Jim Tries to Take the *Hispaniola*

Preview Questions

1. Why do you think Jim wants to go to the *Hispaniola*?
2. How do you think Jim will get to the *Hispaniola*?
3. What do you think will happen to Jim if he gets on board the *Hispaniola*?

Captain Smollett was badly wounded and lay on his bed.

"Will he get better?" I asked the doctor.

"Yes," he said. "But it will take time. Now he must rest. But let me look at that cut on your face."

"It's nothing," I said. Although it was very small, the doctor looked at it and covered it.

"Do you think the mutineers will attack us again?" I asked him.

"No," he said. "They are too few. They know we have pistols. I believe they will go back to the *Hispaniola* and sail away."

"And leave us here?" I said.

"Yes."

Then he went to talk to the squire and the captain. They talked quietly together for a long time, and then the doctor left the stockade.

"Is the doctor mad?" Gray asked me. "Why has he left the stockade?"

"I think," I said, "he may have gone to see Ben Gunn. He is hiding in the forest."

Thinking of Ben Gunn gave me an idea. He had a boat. I did not know how big the boat was or of what kind. I wanted to look at it.

The day was hot. The stockade was even hotter. Everyone was sleepy. I took two pistols and quietly left the stockade. I did not tell the squire I was going. I did not want him to tell me not to go.

The mutineers were in their camp. I could hear them. They were singing. "Good," I thought. "They are probably all drunk."

I moved slowly and quietly through the forest to the shore.

I looked toward the *Hispaniola*. Silver and one of the crew were leaving the ship. They were getting into one of the ship's boats. They were talking to a man wearing a red cap. I heard Silver's parrot cry out. The man in the red cap went into the cabin. The boat moved toward the shore.

"Ben Gunn's boat will be hidden behind a rock," I thought.

I looked behind every large rock. At last, I found his boat. It was very small, but it was big enough for me. My plan was to take it out to the *Hispaniola* and cut her ropes. She would then move toward the shore.

It was not easy to make the small boat go where I wanted it to. It took me a long time to get to the *Hispaniola*. But at last, I could hold the anchor rope. I began to cut it, but the rope was thick and strong.

On board the ship, someone was singing. It was a sad sailor's song. Part of it was, "Only one man left of her crew alive, though the crew that sailed was seventy-five."

The wind now became stronger. The *Hispaniola* began to move through the sea. She nearly pushed my little boat under the water. I was able to get out of her way only just in time.

Then I heard shouting. The two drunken men ran out of the cabin. They knew the ship was moving, but they did not know why.

The sea was now **rough** because of the strong wind. I could not make my little boat go where I wanted it to. I lay at the bottom of my boat.

"Soon this boat will be full of water," I thought. "Then I shall **drown**." I closed my eyes. I thought of home and of the Admiral Benbow.

I slept through the night in my small boat. It was morning when I awoke. I could see a fire burning on the shore. The mutineers were still there.

My boat was now half full of water. The wind was still strong. The *Hispaniola* was moving this way and that way.

"No one is **steering** her," I thought. "The two crew men are either drunk or they have drowned."

I knew what I had to do. I had to get on board the ship and save her.

Slowly I moved my boat toward the ship. It was very difficult. At one moment I was near the ship, the next the sea took me away from her. At last, I was near enough to take hold of the rope. Just then, the wind blew more strongly. Water filled my boat. She sank beneath me as I held on to the rope. I climbed the rope on to the *Hispaniola*.

I soon found the crew. The man with the red cap and Israel Hands were lying near the cabin door. Hands had a bad wound in his leg. He tried to sit up as he saw me, but he could not.

"**Brandy**," he said. "Get me brandy."

I went below. There were empty bottles everywhere. The cabins were very dirty. I found a half-empty bottle of brandy and some food for myself. I went back to Hands and gave him the brandy.

"How badly are you hurt?" I asked him.

"I'll be all right soon," he said.

He drank all of the brandy then slowly sat up.

"That's better," he said. Color began to come back to his face.

"I am now the captain of this ship," I said.

"Yes, Jim," Hands said. "Yes, Captain."

I looked at the man with the red cap.

"Don't worry about him, Jim," Hands said. "He's not drunk. He's dead."

I stood up. "I'm going to take down the pirate flag," I said, "and put up the British flag. This isn't a pirate ship, and I don't want anyone to think that it is."

As I pulled down the **skull and crossbones**, I said, "You must help me sail the *Hispaniola*, Mr. Hands. I want to take her to the north of the island, away from Silver and his mutineers."

"I'll help you, sir," Israel Hands said. "Together we'll sail this ship."

Then he said, "What shall we do with the dead man, Captain? We can't keep him on the ship."

"I'm not strong enough to throw him off the ship," I said. "He'll have to stay where he is."

"I don't like that," Hands said. "It's not good to have a dead man on the ship. And I need a drink, Captain. But the brandy was too strong for me. Wine will be better.

There's wine somewhere on the ship, Captain."

I didn't trust Hands. "Why does he want me to go below?" I thought.

"I don't know where the wine is, Mr. Hands," I said, "but I'll go and look for it."

I went below, but I kept watching Hands. His leg hurt him, but he moved slowly toward some rope. He found a knife there. He picked it up and put it under his shirt. Then he moved slowly back to his old place.

I now knew that Hands could move and that he had a knife.

I found wine in the cabin and took it to Hands. He drank it quickly and said, "We must get this ship to the island, Captain. Do what I tell you, and we'll be there very soon."

I went to steer the ship. As I moved away from him, he got to his feet and came toward me with the knife in his hand.

I pointed my pistol at him. "Stop or I shall shoot," I said.

He kept coming. I tried to shoot him, but the pistol had no powder.

Then the ship was near the shore. The water was very **shallow**. The ship moved on to its side. It was difficult to stand up.

As I put powder into the pistol, Hands threw the knife at me. It went through my shoulder and into the mast of the ship. Hands jumped over the side of the ship into the water. I was alone and unable to move.

Review Questions

1. What happened to Jim's boat?
2. Who was on board the *Hispaniola*?
3. What happened to Jim on board the *Hispaniola*?

Long John Silver in Trouble

Preview Questions

1. How do you think Jim gets away from the ship?
2. What do you think Jim will do?
3. What do you think Long John Silver will do?

I felt very ill. At first, I could not move. The knife was in my skin and in the mast. I pulled and pulled. My skin tore and I was free. I went down to the cabin. I washed the wound and put a piece of clean cloth around it.

There was nothing I could do on the ship. I could not sail her alone. I climbed into the water. It was not deep. I was able to walk slowly toward the shore.

The mutineers were on the other side of the island. I was not far from the stockade where my friends were.

"If I can get to them," I thought, "I can tell them about the ship. They will be able to come here and sail her away."

My wound hurt, but these thoughts helped me to keep going.

When I got to the stockade, I saw a large fire burning inside. This surprised me. Captain Smollett did not like large fires. There was no noise coming from the stockade. No one was on watch. This also surprised me.

Then a voice cried, "Gold! Gold! Gold! Gold!"

I knew it was Silver's parrot. Before I could turn and run, Silver came to the door, a pistol in his hand. "Who's there?" he shouted.

In the light of the fire, he could see me.

"Jim Hawkins!" he said. "I've always liked you, boy, so I'll not hurt you. I'll give you a choice. You can join me, or you can go to your friends—if they'll have you back. They are not pleased with you."

"Where are my friends?" I asked. "What have you done with them?"

"Nothing," Silver said. "Yesterday morning, the doctor came to us with a white flag. 'Let's talk,' he said. 'The ship's gone. None of us can leave the island.' He was right. We looked out to sea. We could not see the *Hispaniola*. 'How many are you?' I asked. 'Four,' he said. 'And one of us is wounded. The boy's gone. We don't know where he is. And that's all I'm going to tell you.'"

"You think you're very clever, Silver," I said. "You think I am a fool and afraid of you. I'm not. You have lost the ship, most of your crew, and the treasure. And why? Because I heard you talking to Dick. I told the doctor about you. I cut the rope. I killed your men on the ship. Kill me if you must, but tell the doctor that I was not afraid of you."

"Kill the boy," shouted one of the men.

"Keep quiet. I'm the captain here," Silver shouted at him. For several minutes, Silver and his men shouted at one another. I thought they might kill him, but at last they were quiet.

"Jim is a good and brave boy," Silver said. "I'll kill any man who touches him." He turned to me. "You've got the ship safe somewhere, haven't you boy?" he said. "There's trouble coming, Jim. But you can trust me."

I was sure I could not trust Silver. And it was difficult to know what he wanted from me. But I was safer with him than with the other mutineers. They wanted me dead.

I looked toward the fire. One of the men had a book. He was doing something to it.

"What are they doing?" I asked Silver.

"We'll soon find out," he said. And he was right.

The five men left the fire and came toward us. One of them put a piece of paper into Silver's hand, then moved back.

Silver looked at it. "The black spot!" he said. "So that's what it's about. You don't want me as your captain. Is that right?"

"Everything has gone wrong," the man said. "You've made too many mistakes. And we shall have to pay for them. We want a different captain."

Silver began to laugh. "You do, do you?" he said. "Then look at this."

He took out a yellow piece of paper and threw it to the ground. The men moved to look at it. I saw what it was. It was the map of the treasure.

"The doctor gave me the map," he said. "Do you want a different captain now?"

"No, no," they shouted. "You're the man for us."

For a time, the trouble was over. The men slept. And so did I.

The next morning, the doctor came to the stockade.

"Good morning to you, Doctor," Silver called. "I have a surprise for you. A young stranger has come to us."

"Jim?" the doctor asked.

"Aye, Jim."

"Is he all right?"

"There's nothing badly wrong with him."

"Good," the doctor said. "I'll look at your wounded men first and talk to Jim afterward."

Several of the crew were sick or had wounds, and the doctor looked at each man.

When he finished looking at the men's wounds, and giving medicine to those who were sick, he said, "Now let me talk to Jim."

"No," shouted one of the mutineers. "You can't trust the doctor. Or the boy."

"If I let you have time with the doctor, Jim," Silver said, "will you promise not to run away?"

"I promise," I said.

The mutineers and Silver now started shouting at one another. They did not know whose side Silver was really on. They thought he was looking after his own future, not theirs.

At last, the men were quiet. Silver walked with me to the wall of the stockade. The doctor was now waiting outside the gate.

"Remember this, Doctor," Silver shouted from the top of the wall. "I saved this boy's life. I know you want to see all of us hang but give me some hope. Be fair to me."

"Are you afraid, John?" the doctor asked him.

"Every man is afraid of the gallows," Silver said and left me on the wall.

I looked down at the doctor.

"It was cowardly of you to run away, Jim," the doctor said.

"I know I did wrong," I said. "But the crew wants to kill me. Only Silver saved me. I know the men will hurt me if they can."

"Why?"

"Because I know where the ship is, and they want to know."

"You know where the ship is!" he said.

I told the doctor about my adventures. As soon as I finished, he said, "Jim, you have again saved all our lives. You found out what the mutineers planned to do. Jump down from the wall, and we'll run for it."

"No, Doctor," I said. "I promised Silver."

At this moment, Silver came back to the wall.

"Let me give you some advice, Silver," the doctor called. "Don't be in a hurry to find that treasure."

"The only way I can save my life, and the boy's," Silver said, "is to find the treasure. But what I don't understand is why you gave me the map."

"I cannot tell you," the doctor said. "It is another man's secret I am keeping. But if we get away from here alive, I'll do my best to save you from the gallows."

And with these words, he walked away.

Review Questions

1. Why did the mutineers give Silver the black spot?
2. Why didn't Jim run from the stockade with the doctor?
3. Why did the doctor tell Silver not to be in a hurry to find the treasure?

CHAPTER
15

Ben Gunn Tells His Story

Preview Questions

1. What do you think one of the mutineers will find?
2. Who do you think will frighten the mutineers?
3. What tree do you think the mutineers were looking for?

Soon after the doctor left, Silver said, "We'll have some breakfast and then we'll go and find the treasure. Then we'll find the ship and sail away."

He smiled at me. "There'll be some of the treasure for you too, Jim."

I didn't trust him. He told different people different stories. He said one thing to his men and another to the doctor. But I knew I was safe only as long as his men trusted him. I hoped the doctor didn't trust him.

We took a boat to the other side of the island. We wanted to find a very tall tree. But we could see many trees ahead of us. We each chose a different one.

When we left the boat, we all went to different trees. I had to go where Silver went. A rope tied me to him. It was not long before we heard a shout.

"That's Morgan," Silver said. "He can't have found the treasure. I'm sure he was going the wrong way."

But we hurried to where Morgan was standing. His face was white.

We looked where he was looking. There was a skeleton on the ground. It was pointing toward a very tall tree.

"Do you think it is Captain Flint's skeleton?" I asked Silver.

"No," Silver said. "Flint killed all his men. This is one of them. He used the body to point to where he buried the treasure. Come on, let's get it."

We walked toward where the skeleton was pointing. As we got near to the tree, a voice sang out, "Fifteen men on the dead man's chest. Yo-ho-ho and a bottle of rum."

All the men turned white they were so afraid. "It's Flint's ghost!" one of them cried.

"No," Silver said. "Someone is playing a trick on us."

"Get the rum! Get the rum!" the voice cried.

"They were Flint's last words," one of the men said. "It is his ghost."

"I wasn't afraid of Flint when he was alive," Silver said, "and I'm not afraid of him now that he's dead. I'm going to get that treasure."

One of the men said, "I don't think it was Flint's voice. I know the voice. It sounds like Flint's voice, but it wasn't his."

"It sounds like Ben Gunn's voice," Silver said.

"Gunn is dead," one of the men argued.

"Dead or alive, I don't care," Silver said. "None of us cares about Ben Gunn. Come on."

We all ran toward where we believed the treasure was.

We found only a huge hole in the ground. The men jumped into the hole and began digging with their hands, but there was nothing in it. The treasure was gone.

The men were so angry that I was afraid for Silver and myself. He knew what was going to happen.

He put a pistol in my hand and said, "Get to the other
side of the hole, Jim. Shoot anyone who tries to attack us."

I thought, "You've changed sides again. How can anyone
trust you?"

The men stopped digging and climbed out of the hole.
They stood on the other side of the hole to us. I knew they
were going to attack us.

"You knew there was no treasure here, Silver," one of them
shouted. "Come on," he said to the others. "Let's kill them."

They began to move toward us. They were just about to
come around from the other side of the hole when there
were three shots. The sound came from the trees. One of

the men fell into the hole. Then Silver fired two shots at them. Another of the men fell. The other three now turned and ran for their lives.

The doctor, Ben Gunn, and Gray came out of the trees and walked toward us.

"You were just in time, Doctor," Silver said. He looked at Ben Gunn. "I thought you were dead."

"I'm not dead, Silver."

"True enough," Silver said. "And you've got the treasure, I'm sure."

"Tell Long John your story, Ben," the doctor said. "The squire is waiting for us at the cave. We'll go and get him and then go down to the shore. There's a boat there we can take to the *Hispaniola*. It's not far from the shore."

As we walked down toward the shore, Ben told his story.

"I was alone here for years," he said. "One day, I found the skeleton. I saw it was pointing to a tree. I dug around that tree and found the treasure. I was living in a cave, so I took the treasure to the cave. This morning, when Long John and his men came looking for the treasure, I showed myself to one of them. He thought I was a ghost." Ben laughed. "He ran off, and this gave me time to get back to the squire and doctor. They were waiting at the cave."

"Now I know," I said to the doctor, "why you gave the map to Silver."

"It was useless by then," the doctor said. "There was no buried treasure. Ben Gunn had it. My plan was to get Long John Silver and his men away from the stockade. We could then get some stores from it."

When we got back to the cave, the squire was waiting

for us.

"Three of the mutineers got away," the doctor told him. "But if we hurry, we can get to the boat before them. They ran back to the stockade on the other side of the island. We are nearer to the boat than they are."

I went into the cave. The captain was lying inside it next to the treasure—a **pile** of gold coins.

"Hello, Jim," he said. "I am pleased to see you. But I don't think you or I will be going to sea again."

That night, we carried the treasure down to the boat. We lit a fire on the shore and had a fine meal together. We were not afraid of the three mutineers. We had pistols. They had none. There were more of us than of them.

The next morning, we went in the boat toward the *Hispaniola*. We did not care about the three men. We left them on the island.

I will not tell you about the journey home. Nothing important happened. But as soon as we got to Bristol, Long John Silver ran away. He took some of the gold with him. None of us cared. We were pleased to see the back of him. We each shared the treasure and used it in a different way.

Review Questions

1. Why did the doctor give the map to Silver?
2. Why did the doctor want to get the mutineers out of the stockade?
3. What happened to the treasure?

NEW WORDS

Chapter 1

sailor *n.* a person who works on a ship

admiral *n.* a naval officer of the highest rank

captain *n.* the leader of a ship

rum *n.* an alcoholic drink made from sugarcane

bar *n.* a place where alcohol is served

chest *n.* a large wooden box with a lock

magistrate *n.* a minor judge

Chapter 2

wounded *adj.* hurt; injured

gallows *n.* the place where people are hanged

Chapter 5

smuggler *n.* a person who hides and moves objects illegally

squire *n.* a person of high social rank in a certain area

brave *adj.* having courage; able to act, even in fear

pirate *n.* a person who robs at sea

cabin boy *n.* a young boy taken on a ship to do jobs such as cleaning and cooking

promise *v.* to tell someone that you will certainly do something

Chapter 6

crew *n.* a group of people that work together on a project

coach *n.* a carriage; a passenger vehicle

aye *adv.* yes

Chapter 7

cabin *n.* a room of a ship

continue *v.* to go without stopping

parrot *n.* a colorful, tropical bird that is capable of copying sounds

ignorant *adj.* unaware of something

gunpowder *n.* a substance made of very small and fine particles used in guns

mutiny *n.* the act of followers going against their leader

Chapter 8

drunk *adj.* having taken too much alcohol

barrel *n.* a large wooden container shaped like a can

Chapter 9

blame *v.* to accuse; to point out the error of someone

mutineer *n.* a person who tries to get a new ship captain by using violence

Chapter 11

guard *v.* to protect; to look out for danger

stockade *n.* a closed area with large posts used for protection

cannon *n.* a very large and heavy gun used on ships

row *v.* to move in the water using paddles or oars

Chapter 13

rough *adj.* in a hard or harsh manner

drown *v.* to die from breathing in water

steer *v.* to change direction by using a round handle

brandy *n.* an alcohol made from wine or cider

skull and crossbones *n.* a black flag with a white skull and two white bones on it used to identify pirates

shallow *adj.* close to the surface; not deep

mast *n.* a long pole used on a ship to support sails

Chapter 15

pile *n.* a large collection of something shaped in a mound

The Trial of Long John Silver

Cast

Judge   Jim Hawkins
Long John Silver   Squire Trelawney
Usher   Captain Smollett

The story does not tell us what happened to Long John Silver. It is possible, however, that he was arrested and taken before a judge.

A courtroom. The judge sits on the bench. A courtroom official and Long John Silver stand facing the judge. Silver is in the dock.

Judge: John Silver, you are charged with mutiny on board the ship *Hispaniola*. What have you to say?

Silver: Not guilty, my Lord.

Judge: Call the first witness, usher.

Usher: Call Jim Hawkins. Call Jim Hawkins.

Jim enters the courtroom and goes to the witness box. The usher hands him a Bible.

Usher: Take the Bible in your right hand and repeat after me. I, Jim Hawkins . . .

Jim: I, Jim Hawkins . . .

Usher: Do promise to tell the truth . . .

Jim: Do promise to tell the truth . . .
Usher: All of the truth and only the truth.
Jim: All of the truth and only the truth.

The usher moves away and sits.

Judge: Now Hawkins, what have you to say?
Jim: I overheard John Silver planning a mutiny.
Judge: Where did you hear this?
Jim: On board the *Hispaniola*.
Judge: What were you doing on the ship?
Jim: I was the cabin boy.
Judge: Where was the ship going?
Jim: We were going to find Captain Flint's treasure.
Judge: And who was Captain Flint?
Jim: He was a pirate.
Judge: I see. So you were going to search for a pirate's treasure.
        Is that right?
Jim: Yes.
Judge: Why? What did you plan to do with the treasure?
Jim: I don't know, sir.
Judge: Did you find the treasure?
Jim: Yes, sir.
Judge: What did you do with it?
Jim: We shared it among ourselves, sir.
Judge: Very interesting. Who were the other people on board
        the *Hispaniola*?
Jim: Doctor Livesey, Squire Trelawney, Captain Smollett, and
        the crew, sir.
Judge: (*to Usher*) Are any of those people here?
Usher: Yes, my Lord. They are waiting to give evidence.

Judge: Very well. You may leave the witness box for the moment, Hawkins. But I may want to question you some more. Usher, call Squire Trelawney.

Usher: Call Squire Trelawney. Call Squire Trelawney.

Squire Trelawney comes into the court room and goes to the witness box. The usher hands him a Bible.

Usher: Take the Bible in your right hand and repeat after me. I, Squire Trelawney . . .

Squire: I, Squire Trelawney . . .

Usher: Do promise to tell the truth . . .

Squire: Do promise to tell the truth . . .

Usher: All of the truth and only the truth.

Squire: All of the truth and only the truth.

The usher moves away and sits.

Judge: What were you doing on board the *Hispaniola*?

Squire: I paid for the ship and employed the captain and crew.

Judge: Was the search for the treasure your idea?

Squire: Yes.

Judge: How did you find out about the treasure?

Squire: Jim Hawkins found a map in a sea captain's chest.

Judge: Did he steal the map?

Squire: No, my Lord. The sea captain was staying at the Admiral Benbow.

Judge: And what is that?

Squire: An inn, my Lord. It is owned by Hawkin's mother. The sea captain, Captain Bones, died. The pirates came to the inn and searched for the map. Hawkins brought it to me because he did not want the pirates to have it.

Judge: What did you do with it?

Squire: I kept it, my Lord. I decided to search for the treasure.

Judge: Why?

Squire: I wanted an adventure. I didn't know what was going to happen.

Judge: What did happen?

Squire: The crew mutinied. They tried to kill us.

Judge: Who was the leader of this mutiny?

Squire: Long John Silver. I thought he was an honest man, but he was not. He lied to me.

Judge: You may leave the witness box, but do not leave the court. I may want to question you some more. Usher, call Captain Smollett.

Usher: Call Captain Smollett. Call Captain Smollett.

Captain Smollett enters the court and walks to the witness box. He takes the Bible from the usher.

Smollett: I promise to tell the truth, the whole truth, and only the truth.

Judge: What can you tell the court about this matter?

Smollett: Squire Trelawney employed me as captain of the *Hispaniola*. I did not know at the time that we were going to search for treasure. I did not choose the crew. Long John Silver chose them. At first, I thought he was an honest man, but I was wrong. He is a pirate. He killed at least four men. He led the mutiny on board the *Hispaniola*.

Judge: Did you find the treasure?

Smollett: A man called Ben Gunn found it. We rescued him from the island. He shared the treasure with us.

Judge: Was it his treasure?

Smollett: No, my Lord. It was Captain Flint's treasure.

Judge: You may leave the witness box, but do not leave the court. I may want to question you some more.

The judge turns to Long John Silver.

Judge: What have you to say, Silver?

Silver: I'm no worse than they are, my Lord. The doctor and the squire were in it with me. We were all after the treasure. We quarreled, that's all. And now they are trying to blame me.

Judge: Did you lead the mutiny?

Silver: The crew wanted to mutiny. They didn't want to share the treasure with the doctor and the squire. The only way I could stop the crew from killing the doctor and the squire was to lead the mutiny. Then I could control the crew. Ask Jim Hawkins, my Lord, if I saved his life.

Judge: Usher, call Jim Hawkins.

Silver: Call Jim Hawkins.

Jim enters the court room and goes to the witness box.

Judge: Don't forget your promise to tell the truth, Hawkins. Now, did Long John Silver save your life?

Jim: I think so, sir. The crew wanted to kill me, but he stopped them.

Judge: Thank you. This is a very interesting case. The treasure belonged to Captain Flint, who is dead. He was a pirate. He stole the treasure from other people. This means that the doctor, the squire, Jim Hawkins, and Captain Smollett shared stolen goods. That is a crime. It makes them as bad as Long John Silver. I must think carefully about this matter.

The judge stands.

Usher: All rise.

Everyone in the court room stands up as the judge leaves.

COMPASS CLASSIC READERS Series

LEVEL 1

- **The Emperor's New Clothes** by Hans Christian Andersen
- **Black Beauty** by Anna Sewell
- **Grimm's Fairy Tales** by Jacob and Wilhelm Grimm
- **Favorite Asian Folk Tales** by Various Authors
- **The Wind in the Willows** by Kenneth Grahame
- **Doctor Dolittle** by Hugh Lofting
- **Just So Stories** by Rudyard Kipling
- **The Jungle Book** by Rudyard Kipling
- **Aesop's Fables** by Aesop
- **The Happy Prince** by Oscar Wilde

LEVEL 2

- **The Arabian Nights** by Various Authors
- **Robin Hood** by Howard Pyle
- **Alice in Wonderland** by Lewis Carroll
- **The Wizard of Oz** by L. Frank Baum
- **The Railway Children** by Edith Nesbit
- **The Secret Garden** by Frances Hodgson Burnett
- **White Fang** by Jack London
- **The Adventures of Tom Sawyer** by Mark Twain
- **Peter Pan** by J.M. Barrie
- **Anne of Green Gables** by Lucy Maud Montgomery

LEVEL 3

- **The Merchant of Venice** by William Shakespeare
- **Treasure Island** by Robert Louis Stevenson
- **King Solomon's Mines** by Henry Rider Haggard
- **The Time Machine** by H.G. Wells
- **Robinson Crusoe** by Daniel Defoe
- **Romeo and Juliet** by William Shakespeare
- **Dr. Jekyll and Mr. Hyde** by Robert Louis Stevenson
- **Frankenstein** by Mary Shelley
- **A Christmas Carol** by Charles Dickens
- **20,000 Leagues Under the Sea** by Jules Verne

LEVEL 4

- **David Copperfield** by Charles Dickens
- **The Thirty-Nine Steps** by John Buchan
- **Oliver Twist** by Charles Dickens
- **Little Women** by Louisa May Alcott
- **Sherlock Holmes** by Sir Arthur Conan Doyle
- **Tales of Mystery & Imagination** by Edgar Allan Poe
- **Around the World in Eighty Days** by Jules Verne
- **The Moonstone** by Wilkie Collins
- **The Prisoner of Zenda** by Anthony Hope
- **Sense and Sensibility** by Jane Austen

LEVEL 5

- **The Invisible Man** by H.G. Wells
- **Shakespeare's Tragedies** by William Shakespeare
- **Shakespeare's Comedies** by William Shakespeare
- **A Tale of Two Cities** by Charles Dickens
- **Vanity Fair** by William Makepeace Thackeray
- **Pride and Prejudice** by Jane Austen
- **Moby Dick** by Herman Melville
- **The Importance of Being Earnest** by Oscar Wilde
- **More Tales of Mystery and Imagination** by Edgar Allan Poe
- **The Hound of the Baskervilles** by Sir Arthur Conan Doyle

LEVEL 6

- **Wuthering Heights** by Emily Brontë
- **Great Expectations** by Charles Dickens
- **Nicholas Nickleby** by Charles Dickens
- **The Three Musketeers** by Alexandre Dumas, père
- **The Phantom of the Opera** by Gaston Leroux
- **Jane Eyre** by Charlotte Brontë
- **Tess of the d'Urbervilles** by Thomas Hardy
- **Classic American Short Stories** by Various Authors
- **Classic British Short Stories** by Various Authors
- **The War of the Worlds** by H.G. Wells